# GROUT SELECTION CLEANING REPAIR & COLORING

# About the Author

Frederick M. Hueston is a certified stone restoration specialist and Architectural Conservator, His Company, NTC Enterprises Inc. of Longwood, Florida offers consulting on all types of stone and tile flooring. He is the director of The National Training Center for Stone & Masonry Trades. He also serves as the Publications and Seminar Director for the Marble Institute of America.

Other Publications by Mr. Hueston

*The Architects Guide to Stone & Tile Restoration/Maintenance
*Stone Restoration/Maintenance Bible
*Marble & Tile-The Selection & Care of Stone & Tile
*Stone Maintenance Manual for Professional Cleaning Contractors
*Stain Removal Field Guide
*Caring For Your Granite Counter Top
*Caring For Your Terrazzo Floor
*Caring For Your Limestone Floor
*Caring For Your Marble Floor
*Caring For Your Ceramic Tile
*Caring for Your Marble Shower and Vanity
*Grout Repair, Cleaning and Coloring
*How To Polish & Restore Marble Vanity & Furniture Tops Video+Manual
*How To Polish & Restore Marble Flooring Video + Manual
*HAZCOM Manual & Compliance Program
*Stone Fabrication- Techniques and Tips
*How to Start & Operate a Successful Marble Polishing Business
*More Customers- Marketing your Service Business
*Stone Restoration Seminar Cassette Program

For information on Mr. Hueston's books, videos and training programs call NTC at 407-834-4800 or E-mail: FHueston@aol.com

**Grout Selection, Cleaning, Repair & Coloring**



Manufactured in the United States of America
ISBN: 1-892690-03-9

Author: Frederick M. Hueston



**NTC Enterprises Inc**
**941 Longdale Ave**
**Longwood, FL 32750**
**407-834-4800**
**Fax 407-834-6610**
**E-Mail: Fhueston@aol.com**
**http://www.ntc-stone.com**

## Publications available from NTC

*Caring for your Marble Shower & Vanity*

*Caring for your Granite Counter Tops*

*Caring for your Marble Floor*

*Caring for your Limestone Floor*

*Caring for Your Terrazzo Floor*

*Caring for Your Ceramic Tile*

*Grout Selection, Cleaning, Repair & Coloring*

*Marble & Tile- The selection and Care*

*How to Start & Operate a Successful Marble Polishing Business*

*How To polish and Restore Marble Vanity and Furniture Tops Video*

*Stain Removal Field Guide*

**To receive our FREE catalog call 407-834-4800**

# TABLE OF CONTENTS

## GROUT SELECTION

Although grout is not a floor tile or paver, it is an important component of the floor. Grout is usually a cement-based material that is used to fill in the spaces between the tile. It is produced in a variety of colors.

There are basically two types of cementitious grout: sanded and unsanded. There are several latex additives that can be mixed with the grout during installation to provide stain resistance. It is advisable to seal your grout with a silicone sealer to prevent staining.

In addition to cement-based grouts there are epoxy grouts, which are made from plastic resins of epoxy and mixed with the grout at installation. They are usually more expensive than cementitious grouts, but are extremely stain resistant. Epoxy grouts are also available in many colors. The short guide which follows should assist you in selecting the proper grouting for your tile.

## GROUT TYPES

Several options are open to you when choosing grout for your tile floor, wall or counter top, and a thorough understanding of them now may spare you some headaches later. Some of the worst problems associated with tile have nothing to do with the tile and *everything* to do with the grout. A beautiful white marble floor, for example, is hardly seen in its best light when the white grout is black and dirty. The basic types of grout are:

**Sanded grout.** This is the type most commonly used for ceramic tile, stone and any tile with a grout joint ⅛″ or larger. Composed of Portland cement, sand and other additives, it is mixed with water and troweled into the grout joint, where it takes approximately 24 hours to dry. Although it becomes as hard as concrete when fully cured, it can pose several problems. It is very absorbent, and if it is not sealed it will soak up stains, dirt and any other liquid spilled on the tile. Care should be exercised in choosing a good sealer to prevent staining and water absorption. Although many grouts can be mixed at the time of installation with a latex additive which will reduce absorbency, I would still recommend sealing. Another problem arises when it is used with marble. Since the grout is made with sand, it *will* scratch polished marble when installed. This is a common problem among tile contractors who are not familiar with stone installation. *Never use sanded grout on polished marble!* Polished marble should be installed with a grout width smaller than ⅛″.

**Unsanded or wall grout.** Unsanded grout, commonly called "wall grout," is essentially sanded grout without the sand. It is used on ceramic tile and polished marble with grout joints smaller than ⅛″. All the cleaning problems associated with sanded grout apply to wall grout, which should be sealed after installation to reduce absorbency.

**Latex-modified grout additives.** Several latex additives are available that can be added to both sanded and unsanded grouts. These additives are blends of acrylics and latex, and will decrease water absorption, increase strength and improve color retention. Some grouts have dried latex powder added to them at the factory and do not require additional additives. A number of manufacturers also include anti-fungal and mildew-resistance additives.

**Epoxy grout.** This type of grout is a water less two-part formula consisting of epoxy resins (Part A) and a hardener (Part B). These components are mixed on-site just prior to grouting. When fully cured, epoxy grouts are stain- and mildew-resistant; they are also less absorbent than cement-based grouts, and are easily cleaned. They should be used on tile and stone on kitchen countertops, back splashes and bathrooms. Epoxy grouts are difficult to apply, and can be quite messy during application; be sure to hire a contractor who is skilled in their use. These grouts require no additional sealer.

**Furan grout.** Furan grouts are similar to epoxies, but are composed of polymers of furfuryl alcohol, which are highly resistant to chemical action. They are rarely used for residential installation, but are often employed in industrial projects, such as laboratories, dairies, meat-packing plants, etc. Furan grouts are only available in black, and special skills are required for proper installation.

## GROUT CLEANING-NEW

The initial cleaning of a new tile or stone floor or wall should be performed by the installation contractor. If the contractor has not performed a final clean-up, or if you installed it yourself, the procedures described in this chapter are absolutely essential.

## EXCESS GROUT CLEAN-UP

A new stone or tile floor may have a slight film due to dust settling from construction or an inadequate clean-up of the grout residue. It is very important that excess grout be removed before it has a chance to dry—within 24 hours for cement grout, and one hour for epoxy grouts. If excess cement grout is left on the surface for more than 24 hours, than use the following procedure:

1. Remove any large chunks of grout with a scraper or razor blade. On polished stone, take particular care not to scratch the surface.

2. Sweep or dust-mop the floor to remove all loose debris.

3. Rinse the floor several times with plain water. Apply the water with a string mop, wrung out tightly. Avoid flooding the tile, as excessive water may cause

discoloration of the grout. If too much water is applied, pick up the excess with a wrung-out string mop or wet vacuum.

4. If grout residue remains after several rinses, it will necessary to use grout-removing chemicals, as follows:

- For marble and stone: Add 3-4 oz of household ammonia to water and rinse the floor several times. A number of non-acidic grout removers are also commercially available

.

- For glazed ceramic or porcelain: Mix a mild solution of 2-4 oz of sulfamic acid and water. Rinse the floor several times. Repeat rinsing with ammonia and water solution to remove acid residue. *Do not use any acid other than sulfamic acid.* There are several grout cleaners on the market which contain sulfamic acid; consult your local stone or tile supplier, or check with the firms and organizations listed in the resource directory at http://www.ntc-stone.com.

*Do not use any acids on polished marble!*

## EPOXY GROUT CLEANUP

Epoxy grouts are made from 100% epoxy resins. They have excellent chemical-resistance properties, and are highly recommended for tile in kitchens and baths as well as countertops and shower walls. If you decide to use an epoxy grout, make sure the person who installs it has experience working these products.

One of the biggest problems with epoxy grouts is failing to clean up the grout residue. Unlike cement-based grouts, which can sit for 24 hours, epoxy grouts need to be thoroughly cleaned *within one hour* or clean-up may prove difficult to impossible, depending on the surface type. If epoxy residue remains, the following procedure is recommended:

1. Scrape any large pieces of epoxy from the surface, using a sharp razor blade. Wetting the area first will help prevent scratching.

2. Mix a solution of hot water (the hotter the better) and several drops of dishwashing detergent (Ivory, Dove, etc.). Apply the solution to the epoxy and scrub with a green scrub-pad.

3. If the soap solution does not remove the epoxy, try wiping the surface with a clean white rag and acetone.

4. If the acetone fails, the epoxy will have to be removed with a stronger solvent such as methylene chloride. Apply the solvent to the epoxy and let it stand for several minutes. Then pick up the solution with clean rags and rinse the area with plenty of water.

*Caution:* Solvents like methylene chloride are very dangerous to work with. If it becomes necessary to use them, I recommend calling in a professional. If you must use them yourself, be sure to have adequate ventilation and wear solvent-resistant gloves and safety glasses. Read and adhere to *all* cautions on product label.

## GROUT CLEANING- OLD

Oh, that awful dirty grout. You've tried everything and it just refuses to come clean. Well help is right here. Most grout becomes soiled by grease and water based stains. In order to remove the dirt it needs to be cleaned with two different cleaners. One will remove the grease and oil and the other will remove the water based soil.
The following is my secret recipe for cleaning grout.

You will need two chemicals. Sulfamic acid

and a good wax floor stripper. Sulfamic acid can be purchased at most home centers and can also be found at most tile supply companies. The floor wax stripper can be purchased at most janitorial supply houses and some of the large price clubs like Sams or Costco. Ask for an alkaline based floor wax stripper.

1. Sweep the floor throughly removing any loose dirt, dust etc. For showers and walls, wipe with a dry rag.

2. Mop the floor with warm water and a good floor cleaner. Ammonia will work also. For showers and walls use a clean rag with the above chemical.

3. Mix a solution of the alkaline stripper in a pail of warm water. Make sure to follow the directions on the bottle.

4. Apply a small amount of this solution to the grout. Allow it to stand for several minutes and agitate with a scrub brush,

toothbrush or similar type brush.
Apply additional solution if it begins to dry.

5. Pick up any excess solution with a mop or a wet vacuum.

6. Rinse the grout with plain warm water.

7. Mix a solution of sulfamic acid with warm water per directions on the label.

8. Apply the acid solution to the grout and agitate.

9. Rinse the grout several times with clean water and allow to dry overnight.

10. Once dry, seal the grout with a good penetrating sealer.

If the above technique does not work then the grout will have to be removed and replaced or if the grout is sound and not falling apart, it can be re-colored.

## GROUT CLEANING MACHINES

For very large areas or for contractors who clean a lot of grout there are several grout cleaning machines available.
The names of these machines are called Grout Hog and RotoWash.

## GROUT REMOVAL & REPLACEMENT

Removing and replacing grout is not that difficult. All it requires is a little patience and the know-how. The following is the know how, you supply the patience and Oh yes, the elbow grease.

You will need the following tools:

-A hand held gout saw. You can purchase these at most home centers, hardware stores or tile supply houses. They usually run a couple of dollars.

-A grout float. Also only a few dollars. I prefer the type with the rubber face, but any grout float will work.

## GROUT REMOVAL PROCEDURE

1. Remove the grout using the grout saw. Work the saw in a back and forth motion until you have removed more than half the grout. It is not necessary to remove all the grout. As long as you remove about 1/4 inch minium.

2. Once the desired amount of grout is removed. Vacuum all the grout and dust from

the floor or wall.
3. Check for loose tile and re-set these before regrouting. You are now ready to re-grout.

## GROUT REPLACEMENT

1. Choose the proper grout. For walls and grout joints 1/8 of an inch or smaller use un-sanded grout. For floors and grout joints over 1/8 of an inch use a sanded grout. Caution: If you have marble tile, unsanded grout can scratch.

2. Place the grout in a bucket, add water and mix into a thick, smooth consitnecy. Do not mix it too soupy. Add more dry grout powder if it gets too soupy. Some grout needs to sit several minutes before using and then remixed. Check with the grout manufactures directions.

3. Apply the grout with the grout float. Work the grout into the joints making sure

they are full. It helps to pack the grout into the joints by pressing hard on the grout float.

4. Once all the grout joints are full, hold the float at a 45 degree angle and move it diagonally across the grout joint to remove excess grout. See photo below. It's best to work in small sections so the grout does not dry too fast.

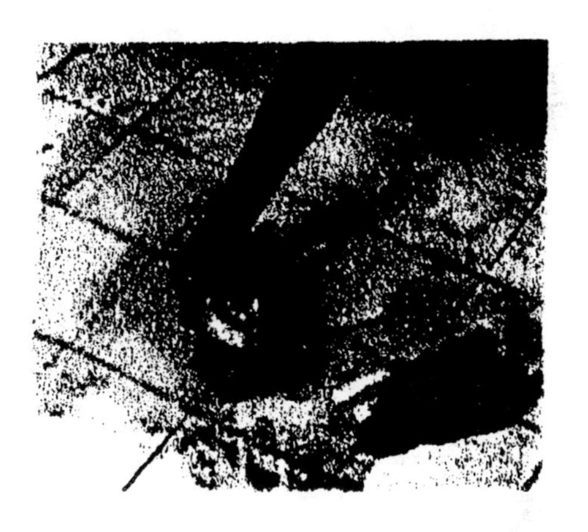

5. Once all the tile is grouted, clean the tile with a clean wet sponge. It will be necessary to rinse several times. I prefer using two buckets and two sponges. Change the water

often.
6. Allow the grout to sit at least 24 hours. Occasionally a light grout film will be present after the grout dries. To remove this film, simply buff with a clean dry cloth.

7. Avoid walking on the floor or using the shower for at least 24 hours.

## GROUT SEALING

In order to keep your new grout or newly cleaned grout clean, it should be sealed. There are so many sealers on the market today. Which one's are best? Which ones really work?

It can be very confusing trying to choose a sealer to protect grout. In the past several years the janitorial industry have bombarded the market with hundreds of products to seal

& protect grout.
Fortunately, all of these products fall into only two major categories:

1. coatings
2. impregnators or penetrating sealers.

**Coatings:**
Coatings are sealers that place a sacrificial coating on the surface of the grout. This is a film that lays on top of the grout acting as a barrier to prevent water, oil and dirt from entering the pores.

Coatings can be classified into two general types:

1. strippable
2. permanent.

**Strippable coatings**:
Strippable coatings are coatings that are designed to be easily stripped or removed from the surface of the grout. These coatings are made of polymers consisting of acrylics,

styrene, polyethylene and others. They are usually water based. Many of the janitorial products are water based polymer type coatings. To identify these coatings look for terms on the label such as "metal cross link","high solids","high speed", "acrylic", "thermoplastic", etc. When in doubt, ask. There are hundreds of different formulas of strippable coatings.

**Permanent coatings:**
Permanent coatings are coatings that are very difficult to remove. They are made of solvent based polymers such as polyurethane, epoxies, etc. These are not recommended for grout.

**Impregnators or penetrating sealers:**
Impregnators are designed to penetrate below the surface of the grout and deposit solid particles in the pores or to coat the individual minerals below the surface. Water, oil and dirt are restricted from entering.
Impregnators can be solvent or water based

and usually contain silicone, siloxane, silane, methyl silicate or other similar silicon derivatives.

Impregnators can also be classified into two types:

1. hydrophobic- water repelling
2. oilophopic- oil repelling.

**Hydrophobic impregnators**
Hydrophobic impregnators are designed to repel only water and water based chemicals. Fruit drinks, coffee, tea, soda, etc. would be repelled by a hydrophobic impregnator.

**Oilophobic impregnators**
Oilophobic impregnators are designed to repel water and oil based liquids. Cooking oil, grease, body oils, etc. would be repelled by a oilophobic impregnator.

An oilophobic impregnator will always be hydrophobic, but a hydrophobic impregnator may not be oilophobic. Be sure to read product labels carefully to determine if they are hydrophobic or oilophobic. Some products are listed as oil resistant. Oil resistant and oil repellant are entirely different. Oil resistant will only slow down the absorption of oil into the grout. Oil repellant will prevent oil from entering the grout. Again, read product labels carefully. Be sure you are buying the right product for your particular situation.

## COATING OR IMPREGNATOR?

How do you make the determination between a coating or an impregnator? They both have their advantages and their disadvantages. The following summary should be studied carefully when choosing the proper product:

**Coating-Advantages;**

Coatings are sealers that place a protective, sacrificial layer on the surface of the grout.

1. Coatings are generally economical. The initial application is relatively low.
2. Coatings are difficult to apply since you must apply them with a brush or applicator, which can be very tedious.
3. Coatings generally will provide a sacrificial coating. This layer will take most of the wear, preventing wear of the grout

**Coatings-Disadvantages**

1. Since most coatings are typically softer than the grout itself, they will usually scratch, mar and scuff very easily, showing traffic patterns soon after application. This will require re-application.
2. Coatings can build up and can cause an unsightly appearance, producing an unnatural look.
3. Poor quality coatings can turn yellow. This is especially true if the grout is exposed to UV light.
4. Coatings require frequent stripping and reapplication. The chemicals and abrasives used in the stripping process may cause

damage to the grout. Typically, certain stripping pads and stripping brushes can also cause damage.
5. Certain coatings may block the breathing capability of the grout. Moisture can become trapped below the surface and may lead to the grout falling apart

**Impregnators-Advantages**
1. Most impregnators will not change the appearance of the grout.
2. Most impregnators do not require frequent applications. Since the impregnator is below the surface, it will generally last several years before reapplication is necessary.
3. Most impregnators are not affected by UV light since they are below the surface where UV light cannot penetrate. For this reason they can be used outdoors.
4. Impregnators are typically hydrophobic, while some are oiliophobic.

**Impregnators-Disadvantages**

1. Impregnators that are solvent-based produce noxious and flammable vapors during application.
2. Solvent-based impregnators are harmful to the environment producing high VOC (volatile organic compounds). For this reason, some are restricted in certain states. Always check the MSDS sheet.
3. The initial cost of most impregnators is relatively high.
5. Impregnators in general cannot be used below grade to resist hydrostatic pressure.

When choosing the proper product for protection, the above guidelines should help. Always talk with the manufacture or distributer, and let them know where you plan to use their product. They can be very helpful if you tell them all the conditions that apply.

## GROUT SEALING-PENETRATING

1. Clean the grout throughly with a good grout cleaner or using the cleaning procedure described in this book. Allow the grout to dry throughly.

2. Pour a small amount of sealer on the floor and spread with a string mop or lambs wool applicator. For showers and walls use a terry cloth rag to apply the sealer.

3. Allow the sealer to penetrate into the grout for several minutes. Apply additional sealer if needed.

4. Once all the sealer is applied, buff any remaining sealer from the tile with a dry cloth. If you are sealing a large area, a floor machine may be used.

5. Try to avoid spilling anything on the grout for several days. Some sealers take this long to cure. However, you can walk on the floor once it is buffed.

## GROUT SEALING-COATING

1. Clean the grout throughly with a good grout cleaner or using the cleaning procedure described in this book. Allow the grout to dry throughly.

2. Apply the sealer with a small brush or applicator. Some sealers come with a self dispensing applicator. Work in small areas and avoid getting any sealer on the tile. It helps to keep a clean rag handy in case you accidentally get some on the tile.

3. Allow the sealer to dry throughly before walking on the floor or using the shower.

As you see, this procedure is very time consuming. I prefer the penetrating type for this reason.

## GROUT COLORING

Yes, it is possible to change the color of your grout without replacing it. Coloring your grout also will seal it preventing it from getting soiled.

Before you can coloring your grout you must clean it and perform an adhesion test to make sure the grout coloring will stick and not peel.

Grout coloring can be purchased at most home centers and tile supply houses.

The following adhesion test must be performed before coloring the grout.

**Grout Coloring Adhesion Test.**

1. Clean about one foot of grout using the grout cleaning procedure in this book.

2. Dry the area with a hair dryer or heat gun. Make sure the grout is throughly dry.

3. Apply a small amount of grout coloring with a paint brush to the cleaned area.

4. Dry the grout coloring with the hair dryer. It is best to allow it to dry overnight if time permits.

5. Once the color is dry, take a piece of masking tape and apply it to the grout color. Rub the tape with your finger to make sure it sticks to the color.

6. Now, quickly remove the tape. If the grout coloring sticks to the tape, then the chances it wont stick. In this case you will have to try acid washing the grout and repeating this test. If the coloring remains on the grout, then you can proceed to coloring.

## GROUT COLORING PROCEDURE

1. Make sure you have cleaned the grout and have performed the adhesion test as outlined above.

2. Apply the grout coloring to the grout with a small paint brush or applicator. Do not apply to heavily. It is best to apply two thin coats then one heavy coat.
If you have an air brush, grout coloring can also be applied with it.

Do Not worry about getting the color on the tile. It should clean off easily on ceramic tile. Marble, granite and stone may be a problem. Check to make sure the grout coloring does not absorb into the stone. If it does it may be necessary to mask the tile.

3. Allow the coloring to dry. See label instructions for dry times.

4. Once dry, remove the excess coloring from the tile surface with a green scrub pad and some warm water and dish detergent. If any coloring is removed you can touch up later.

Its that simple. Just take your time.

## GROUT MAINTENANCE

To keep your grout looking new, it is best to avoid harsh cleaners. I recommend a neutral cleaner. A neutral cleaner is not acid or alkaline and has a Ph of 7. Neutral cleaners can be purchased from most janitorial supply houses.

It is especially important to use mild cleaners with colored grout. The coloring will eventually come off and will require re-application.

## GROUT PROBLEMS

**I just installed new grout and after 24 hours it is all turning powdery. What can I do to fix it?**

There are many reasons why the grout becomes powdery. If the tile is very absorbent it will soak up most of the moisture from the grout preventing it from curing properly. Too much water added to the grout mix can also make the grout powdery. To repair the grout you should replace it with new grout. This time wet the floor before installing, this will prevent the grout from drying too fast. Also I would use a latex additive in the grout mix.

**I just completed cleaning a tile floor and the grout is covered with streaks and spots. I am sure it is not the cleaner. How can I repair the grout?**

Short of removing it and installing new grout I would try cleaning it with a neutral cleaner. Be sure to use a soft brush and scrub the grout lines throughly. If this does not throughly clean the grout you may need to replace it.

The spotting you describe may only be moisture in the grout. Before attempting any repair, allow the grout to dry for several days. If the spotting remains after this time then try cleaning.

**I just installed new grout and it is getting a white powdery residue on the surface of the grout.**

This is a condition known as efflorescence. There are soluble salts in the grout coming to the surface. The large amount of water you used dissolved the salts and they are depositing on the surface. Efflorescence will eventually disappear when the floor and the grout is completely dry. Wait several days and mop the grout joints with a neutral cleaner and very little water. Avoid wetting the floor too much, since that will only dissolve more salts causing further efflorescence.

**Can I replace missing grout without removing all the grout? How do I match the color of the existing grout?**

Yes, you can replace the missing grout. Matching the color of the existing grout can prove difficult since grout color will fade over time. The best way is to obtain grout samples from your local tile store and bring them to the job and compare the samples with the grout.

To match the grout it may be necessary to color all the grout. If you choose this option, allow the grout to cure for at least 24 hours.